Knowing Science®

3-DIMENSIONAL TEACHING & LEARNING

GRADE 5

Physical Science Activity Book

D1401620

Knowing Science®
3-DIMENSIONAL TEACHING & LEARNING

GRADE 5

Physical Science Activity Book

Developed by

William Banko, M.D.

Dario Capasso, Ph.D.

Editors

Sarah McGinnis

Lesley Quattrone

Written by

Jennifer Baxter

Sarah McGinnis

Helen Pashley, Ph.D.

Jeffrey S. Schwartz

Advisors

Michael E. Jabot, Ph.D.
Professor, Science Education
Director, Institute for Research in Science Teaching
State University of New York at Fredonia

Thomas O'Brien, Ph.D.
Professor, Science Education
Binghamton University, Graduate School of Education
Binghamton, New York

Knowing Science, LLC - Armonk, NY USA
www.knowingscience.com

Cover and Teachers Manual Design:

Page Designs Inc.

www.pagedesignsinc.com

Knowing Science®, Kid Knowledge®, STEM Knowledge®, STEM Kit®, Eco Cube®, and
Knowing Math® are registered trademarks of Knowing Science LLC.

Patents Pending

Table of Contents

GRADE 5

Physical Science Activity Book

Unit 1 Structure, Properties, and Interactions of Matter

1.1 Weighty Measures — A Review of Weight and Measurement

VOCABULARY

Balanced: *(adj.)* Stability produced by even distribution of forces.

Digital scale: *(noun)* An electronic device used to measure the weight or mass of an object or substances. The result is shown as numbers on a display.

Double pan balance: *(noun)* A device used to measure the weight or mass of an object or substances. A double pan balance has two pans on which the weights are placed. The balance compares the two weights and the result is expressed by an arrow moving on the scale.

Unit: *(noun)* A quantity chosen as a standard in terms of which other quantities of the same kind may be expressed.

Weight: *(noun)* The force with which an object is pulled by gravity.

1.2 Matter is Made up of Small Particles

VOCABULARY

Elements: *(noun)* Each of more than one hundred substances that cannot be chemically broken down into simpler substances and are primary constituents of matter.

Matter: *(noun)* Everything that occupies space and has mass.

Particles: *(noun)* A minute portion of matter.

 **1.3 States of Matter — Nothing Gets Lost**

VOCABULARY

Gas: *(noun)* State of matter that has definite weight but takes the whole volume of the container that holds it.

Liquid: *(noun)* State of matter that has definite weight and volume but takes the shape of any container that holds it.

Matter: *(noun)* Everything that occupies space and has mass.

Particles: *(noun)* A minute portion of matter.

Solid: *(noun)* State of matter that has definite weight, volume and shape.

States of matter: *(noun)* One of the distinct forms that matter takes on. The most common are solid, liquid, and gas.

Water vapor: *(noun)* Fine particles of mist or steam that can be seen hanging in the air.

Activity Sheet 1: Does the Mass Change?

Name: _____

Directions: Using the data recorded in the classroom, complete the table below. Then plot the data on the two bar graphs and answer the questions.

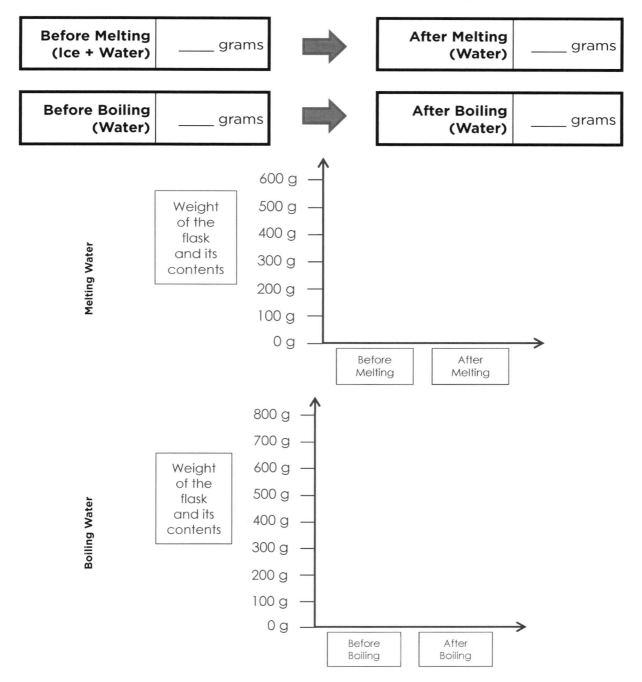

1. Compare the heights of the bars in the Melting Water bar graph. What does this tell you about the mass Before Melting and After Melting?

_____

_____

_____

_____

_____

2. Compare the heights of the bars in the Boiling Water bar graph. What does this tell you about the mass Before Boiling and After Boiling?

_____

_____

_____

_____

3. In your own words, describe the difference between an open and closed system. Was the flask with melting water an open system or a closed system? What about the flask with the boiling water? Explain.

_____

_____

_____

_____

_____

_____

 **1.4 Properties of Matter**

VOCABULARY

Conductor: *(adj.)* The capacity of a material to transmit a form of energy.

Electrical charges: *(noun)* Property of matter that causes it to experience an electrical force. There are two types of electric charges: positive and negative. Like charges repel and unlike attract.

Electrical conductivity: *(noun)* The ability to conduct electricity. The more electricity a conductor transmits, the better the conductor.

Heat conductivity: *(noun)* The ability to conduct heat. The more heat a conductor transmits, the better the conductor.

Insulator: *(noun)* A material that does not easily allow transmitting a form of energy. A bad conductor.

Magnet: *(noun)* A piece of matter that attracts iron or steel. Magnets always have two ends, or poles, called north and south.

Opaque: *(adj.)* Not clear enough to let light through; not transparent.

Reflect: *(verb)* To throw back heat, light, or sound from a surface.

Translucent: *(adj.)* Clear enough to let some light through.

Transparent: *(adj.)* Clear enough to let all the light through.

Activity Sheet 1: Properties of Matter

Name: _____

Directions: Follow the instructions for each experiment below. Then answer the related questions.

Station #1: Light

1. Hold the laser close to each of the materials, one by one. Determine whether each sample is opaque (light does not go through), transparent (light goes through with little change), translucent (only some light goes through), or reflects light like a mirror.

2. Record the results in the table below.

	Plastic wrap	Aluminum foil	Wax paper
Opaque			
Transparent			
Translucent			
Reflects light			

3. Was there a difference in the amount of light that traveled through the various materials?

_____

_____

_____

_____

4. What conclusions can you draw from this investigation?

_____

_____

_____

_____

_____

_____

Station #2: Thermal conductivity

1. At this station, you will find a bucket with warm or hot water, one metal and one plastic tumbler filled with room temperature water, and three thermometers.

2. Record the temperature of each thermometer in the table below (don't forget to include the unit!). The thermometers inside the two cups should be at about the same temperature, while the one in the bucket should have a higher temperature. If this is not the case, let your teacher know.

Bucket	Metal Cup	Plastic Cup

3. Partially submerge the metal and plastic tumblers in the bucket of warm water without letting any water from the bucket enter the tumblers.

4. Wait about 5 minutes for the thermometers to reflect the new temperatures. Meanwhile, write your predictions about the outcome of the experiment below: What will happen to the temperature inside the two tumblers? Will there be any difference between the temperatures of the two tumblers? Why do you think that?

_____

_____

5. A material that allows heat go through easily is called a thermal conductor, while a material that does not let heat go through is called a thermal insulator. For example, the walls of a house are made of insulators; so if it is cold outside and warm inside, almost no heat can escape, keeping the inside warm. Alternatively, a pot is made from a conductor, so the heat from the stove can reach the food cooking inside the pot.

6. After 5 minutes have passed, record the temperatures of the two tumblers and the bucket in the table below.

Bucket	Metal Tumbler	Plastic Tumbler

7. What can you conclude from this investigation?

_____

8. If you are bringing soup to school for lunch, would you rather store it in a metal container or a plastic container? Why?

_____

_____

Station #3: Electrical conductivity

1. Touch the two wires of the Conductivity Tester together. What happens?

_____

_____

2. Using the Conductivity Tester, you are going to test whether electricity travels through each material in your collection. A Conductivity Tester is an open circuit containing a battery and lightbulb. The lightbulb cannot light up until the circuit is closed, forming a loop. Only in a closed circuit can the current travel from one side of the battery to the other side, crossing the whole circuit. A conductor, a material that lets current pass through, can be used to close a circuit in place of a wire. An insulator, a material that does not let current go through, will block the circulation of current, just like when the circuit is open.

3. Select one object from the collection of objects at this station and place the ends of both wires on the object, making sure that the wires don't touch each other. If the lightbulb turns on, the material is a conductor. If the lightbulb does not turn on, the material is an insulator. Follow the same procedure for each of the objects in the collection, and record the results in the table below.

Material	Conductor?	Insulator?

4. What conclusions can you draw from this experiment?

_____

_____

_____

_____

_____

_____

Station #4: Magnets

1. Put the ring magnet stand on a leveled surface, like a table. Place the ring magnets on the stand in such way that they all repel each other. Make a diagram of the stand with the sequence of magnets you chose.

2. Predict which objects from the samples provided at this station will be attracted by the bar magnet and which objects will not.

Attracted:	
Not attracted:	

3. Using the bar magnet, test each material in your collection and record your answers in the table below.

Attracted:	
Not attracted:	

4. Were any of your predictions correct? What are your conclusions?

_____

_____

_____

5. Can you think of a reason the magnet did not attract certain metals?

_____

_____

_____

Station #5: Electric Charges

1. Repeatedly rub the rod with the silk cloth or a sweater. By doing this, you are adding electrical charges to the rod.

2. Move the rod over the bits of paper without touching them. What happens?

_____

_____

_____

3. If a sink is available, turn on the faucet to produce a tiny stream of water. Place the charged rod close to the stream without touching the water. What happens?

_____

_____

_____

4. Rub the charged rod with an aluminum sheet. Move the rod over the bits of paper without touching them. What happens now?

_____

_____

_____

Activity Sheet 2: What's What?

Name: _____

Directions: Read the following text about properties of matter, then proceed with testing the properties of each ball assigned. Once you evaluated the properties of the assigned set of balls, write down three questions that should help you to identify the mysterious ball that was hidden by the teacher.

Properties of Matter

Have you ever played tennis? Or have you watched a tennis match on television? In a televised tennis match, sportscasters sometimes announce how fast the ball travels. When a player serves a tennis ball, it usually travels over 120 mph. However, when a bowler throws a bowling ball down the lane, it will not reach a speed of 120 mph, nor would we want it to.

Can you think of other sports where some kind of ball serves as the focus of attention during a game? There are many. Football, baseball, softball, basketball, ping pong, golf, and rugby are examples. Yet, the balls used in each of these sports are quite different from one another. Each ball has its own characteristics; in other words, it has its own physical properties. Some are small and some are big; all are round except for the football and rugby ball. They are made from different materials, have different weights, and feel differently in your hands. Tennis balls are fuzzy, while bowling and billiard balls are hard and smooth. Some are lightweight, such as ping pong balls, and others are very heavy like bowling balls.

Generally, when we see different types of objects that look different, feel different and have different characteristics, we like to say that these objects have different physical properties.

Scientists classify materials by their properties. We can identify these physical characteristics—or properties of matter—with our senses. Properties of matter are somewhat like the special physical qualities that each of your friends has. For instance, one of your friends may have blue eyes, and another may have brown eyes. Some of your friends may be tall for their age group, and others may be of average height. Similarly, objects vary in their characteristics. They look different, feel different, and taste different.

We often want to study properties of objects in detail, and tools exist that can assist us in the study. If you want to study an insect up close in order to see its anatomy, you could use a magnifying lens or a microscope. If you want to see if a particular object is attracted to a magnet, you need a magnet to test the item. Anything that helps you accomplish the task can be used as a tool. Tools that commonly help us study the property of matter include hand lenses, metric rulers, thermometers, balances, magnets, circuit testers, graduated cylinders, and so on.

When manufacturing products, it is important to know the properties of various kinds of matter so that we can choose the proper material for a specific use. Think what technology would be like without the knowledge and the measurement of specific properties. Electric wires made of wood would not conduct electricity, garden furniture made of ice would melt under the sun, elastic bands made of rigid plastic would not extend. Nothing would really work! For this reason, scientists study and measure the properties of every new material they discover so it is possible to classify materials according to specific properties. This allows us to select the proper material to make what we need.

Using the materials provided at each station, design an experiment to test the properties of the 3 balls. Then complete the table below.

Station #1: Laser
The laser can be used to determine if a material is transparent, opaque, or reflects light.

Station #2: 1 Small bucket of warm water and a metal tumbler
The metal tumbler conducts heat from the warm water to whatever is inside the tumbler, quickly warming up any conductor in the tumbler.

Station #3: Conductivity Tester
The Conductivity Tester verifies whether an object closes the circuit (is a conductor) or does not close the circuit (is an insulator).

Station #4: 1 Magnet
The magnet either interacts or does not interact with a material.

		Wood	Steel	Acrylic
Light	Transparent			
	Opaque			
	Reflect light			
Thermal conductivity	Conductor			
	Insulator			
Electrical conductivity	Conductor			
	Insulator			
Magnets	Attracted by magnets			

Questions to guess what kind of ball was hidden:

1. _____

2. _____

3. _____

1.5 Can Matter Change?

VOCABULARY

Chemical change: *(noun)* Change caused by a chemical reaction changing one substance into another.

Irreversible: *(adj.)* A chemical or a physical change that cannot be undone.

Mixture: *(noun)* A substance made by mixing other substances together without any of them changing.

Physical change: *(noun)* A change regarding the physical properties of a material. The material is still the same kind of matter (no chemical change occurred).

Reversible: *(adj.)* A physical or a chemical change that can be undone.

Activity Sheet 1: A Mixture

Name: _____

Directions: Using the data recorded in the classroom, complete the table below. Plot the data on the two bar graphs, and answer the questions that follow.

Complete the table using the data collected in the classroom (don't forget to include the units!):

	Mass
32-oz. container with lid	
Container with sand	
Container with water	
Empty sand container	
Empty water container	
32-oz. container with mixture of sand and water	

Evaluate the total mass of the Water + Sand mixture using the table below (don't forget to include the units!):

_____ − _____ = _____
Mass of   Mass of   Mass of
Container with sand   Empty sand container   Sand

_____ − _____ = _____
Mass of   Mass of   Mass of
Container with water   Empty water container   Water

_____ − _____ = _____
Mass of Container +   Mass of 32-oz. container   Mass of Water +
Sand + Water   with lid   Sand Mixture

In the following bar graph, plot the mass of the two components (sand and water) of the mixture using the same column ("Before mixing"). Then, draw a second bar above "After mixing" to show the total mass of the mixture, as calculated in the table on the previous page.

(On the right, you can see an example of how to set up your bar graph. The example measurements <u>DO NOT</u> represent the data you should obtain from the classroom measurements.)

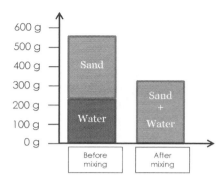

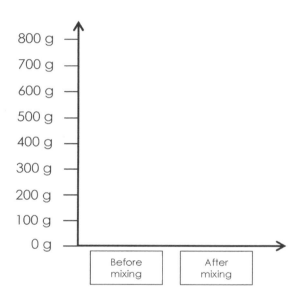

1. What do you observe from the graph above? Is the amount of matter changed during the mixing?

_____

_____

2. Describe what a physical change is.

_____

_____

_____

Activity Sheet 2: Matter Changes

Name: _____

Directions: Follow the instructions below to experiment with chemical changes. Then complete Part 2 when your teacher asks you to.

Part 1

1. Pour 1 tsp. of water inside the test tube and then carefully add 1/4 tsp. of vegetable oil. Close the tube with a stopper.

2. One student in the group should hold the test tube firmly with his/her index finger pressing against the stopper to keep it tightly closed, while he/she shakes it once.

3. Wait a minute or so and observe any changes.

4. Now, open the test tube carefully, slowly adding 1/4 tsp. of soap, then close the test tube again. Without shaking the tube, ask one volunteer from your group to weigh the test tube with the three liquids, and record the result.

Test tube weight (before shaking) _____

5. Now, shake the tube to mix the three liquids (follow the procedure from step 2).

6. Observe the test tube for about 2 minutes. Then weigh the test tube again.

Test tube weight (after shaking) _____

Do you see any change? Does the oil separate again now that you have added soap?

_____

_____

_____

_____

Complete the following bar graph with the collected data.

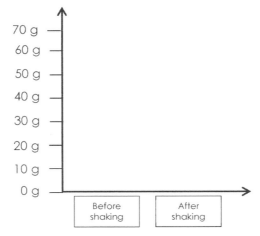

Part 2

1. Do you think the change happening in the polymer after adding water is a physical change or a chemical change? Explain your reasoning.

    _____

    _____

    _____

    _____

    _____

    _____

    _____

2. List some chemical changes that might take place around your house.

    _____

    _____

    _____

Made in the USA
Columbia, SC
26 October 2017